DAVID DAVID

POP

COLORING

BOOK

A COLLECTION OF PATTERNS DESIGNED BY

DAVID SAUNDERS

WWW.DAVIDDAVID.CO.UK

conran OCTOPUS

I created the first David David geometric print out of necessity. Wanting to make my mark at exclusive art, fashion, and music parties in the early 2000s but unable to find simple yet striking clothes in stores, I did what any resourceful painter would do: I made my own! Masking tape and fabric paints = straight lines and bold colors; a technique I'd developed at art school. Before long it was obvious that my T-shirts struck a chord with my contemporaries and David David was born.

Why David David? After studying Fine Art at Chelsea College of Art in London I moved to Brick Lane, in London's East End, and socialized most nights at a pub called The Golden Heart, on the corner of Hanbury Street. It was frequented by a number of artists and was an awesome hang-out for a recent art graduate. I knew that a few Davids drank there, but, sitting around a table one evening, my companions and I were astonished to find that all seven of us were Davids. We needed nicknames, and mine was Dave Dave. Later, when it came to naming my brand, Dave Dave sounded too informal, so David David it was.

Fast forward to the present day, and the same distinctive David David prints have adorned the walls of the Victoria and Albert Museum in London, and been worn by the musician Kanye West, the artist Sam Taylor-Johnson, and the model Agyness Deyn.

My latest project is this; the first David David coloring book. I hope you have as much fun with color as I have always done. Tap into your creative side, step into an artist's shoes, and follow your instincts to make the prints POP. I have put some tips for pairing-up colors at the start of the book. For a sense of energy, use bright, bold palettes with zippy, powerful red hues. For something calmer, work with subtle pastel colors. Explore lots of different color palettes to see if you get a different feeling from each—maybe even recreate the same patterns in a variety of colorways.

If you are interested in creating your own geometric patterns, I have also included a guide to drawing equilateral triangles. It might seem simple, but the humble triangle is the building block for most geometric prints. Triangles lend themselves to tessellation. For me, this repetition has always been a big part of the appeal of geometric prints. Perhaps I am drawn to reflection and symmetry because I am a twin. Whatever the reason, I found creating patterns instinctive from an early age. Even at infant school I embroidered triangles, not teddy bears like my friends did.

Whatever you decide to do, please share it with me! I can't wait to see your work.

David Saunders

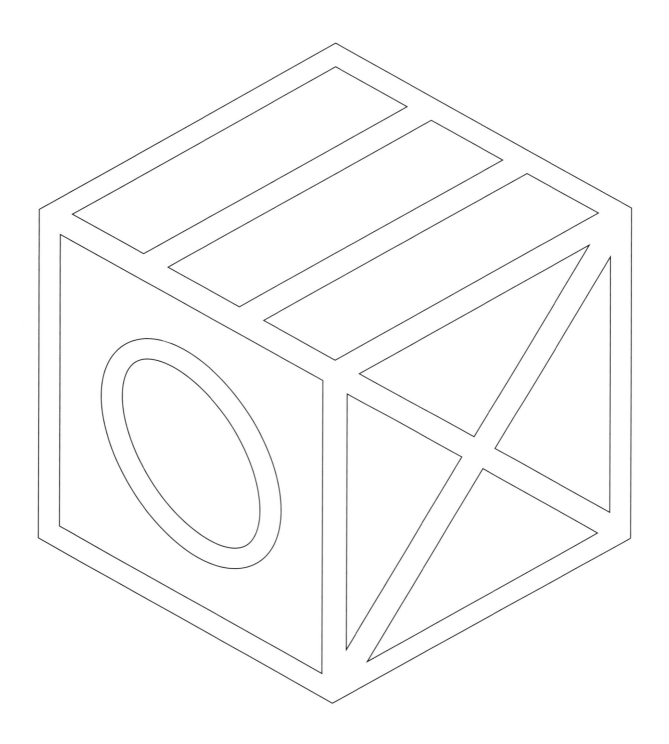

BLOCKER PLATE

ALISON GETS A GOLD STAR

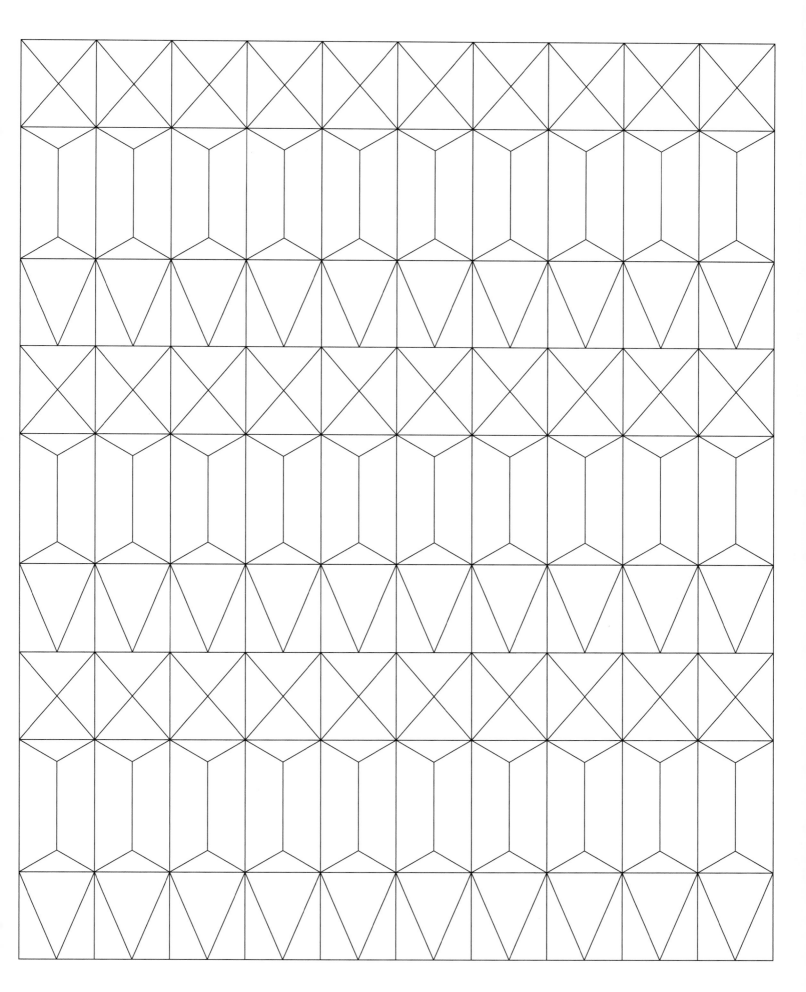

CASTLE

PETRICHOR

YOUNG FRIEDA

HEXAGON'S ORIGIN

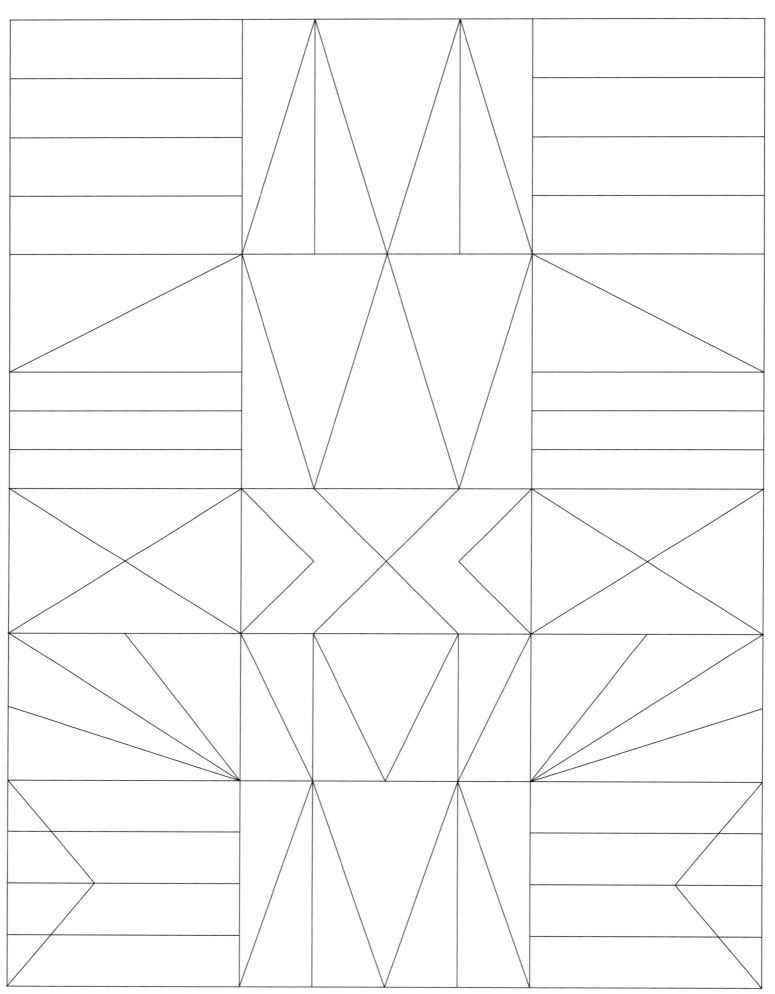

BUILT TO LAST

CORE BLIMEY

ROBERTA AND BITS

CAROUSEL METEOR

ZAP

TERI, DID I TELL YOU YOU WERE AWESOME?

BLOCKER

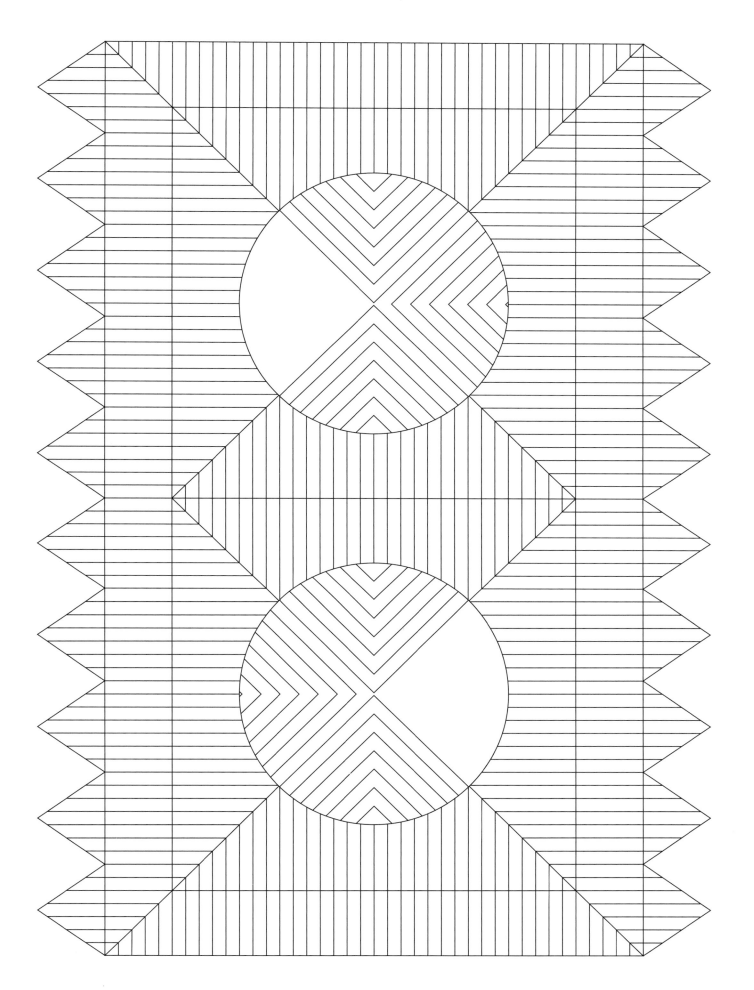

MIKEY MIKE

ICE CREAM

HEXAGON COLONY

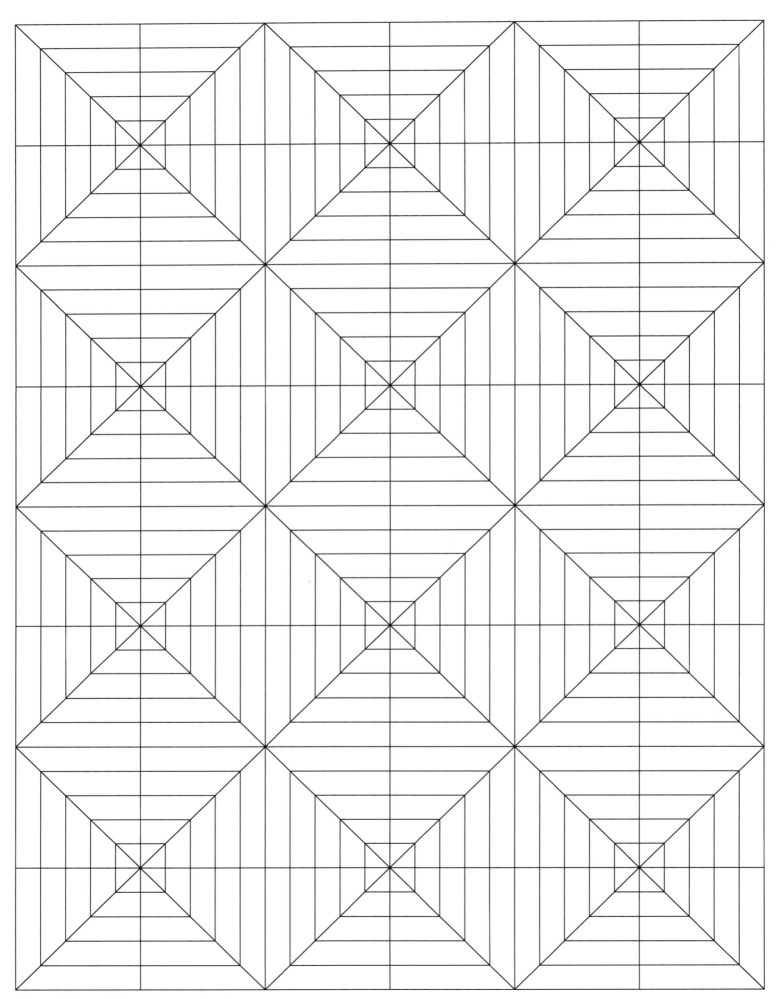

SNAP AND REPEAT

TOBY'S STAR

THE BIG D

WRONG TURN

NEAT

DOUBLE DICE

ZEBRA CROSSING

FIRST A ZIG AND THEN A ZAG

CAROUSEL CORE

MEDALLION

ERIN ERIN

LUCY

MICRO AURORA

WANDERLUST

SCARAB

JUPITER

CUBE

EFFERVESCENCE

DALIA DALIA

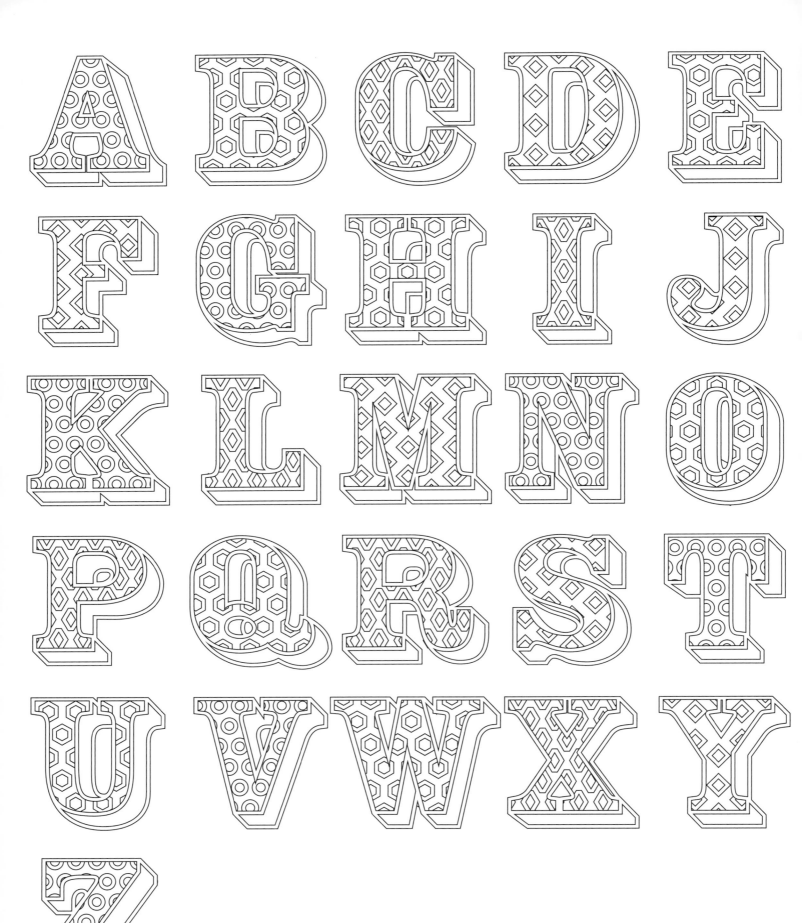

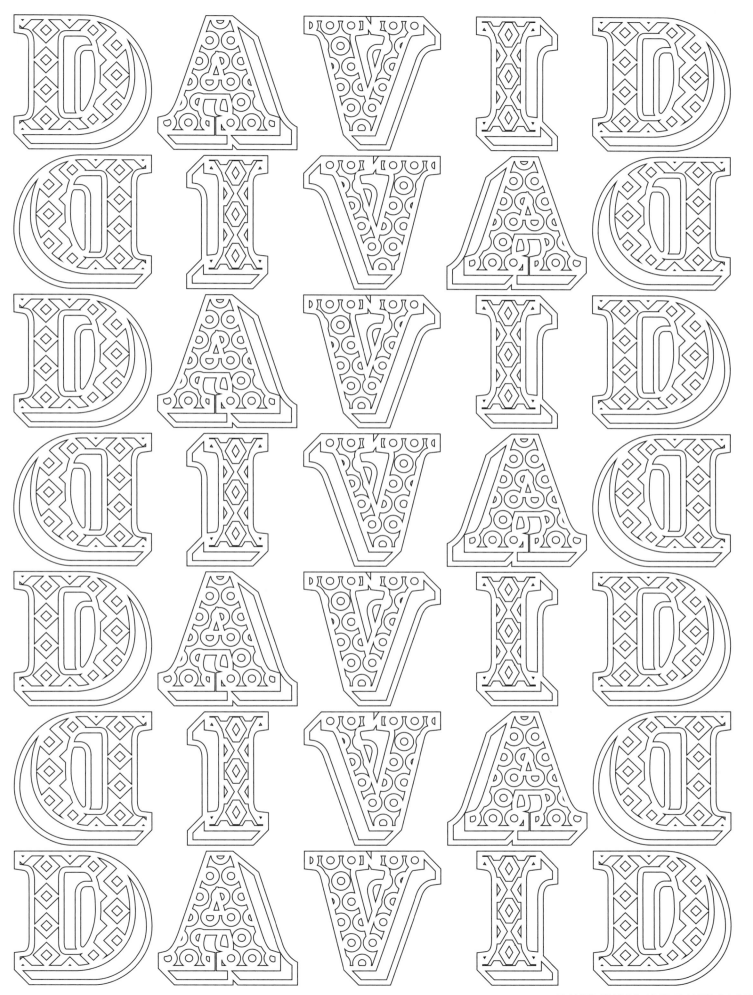

FRONT PINEAPPLE

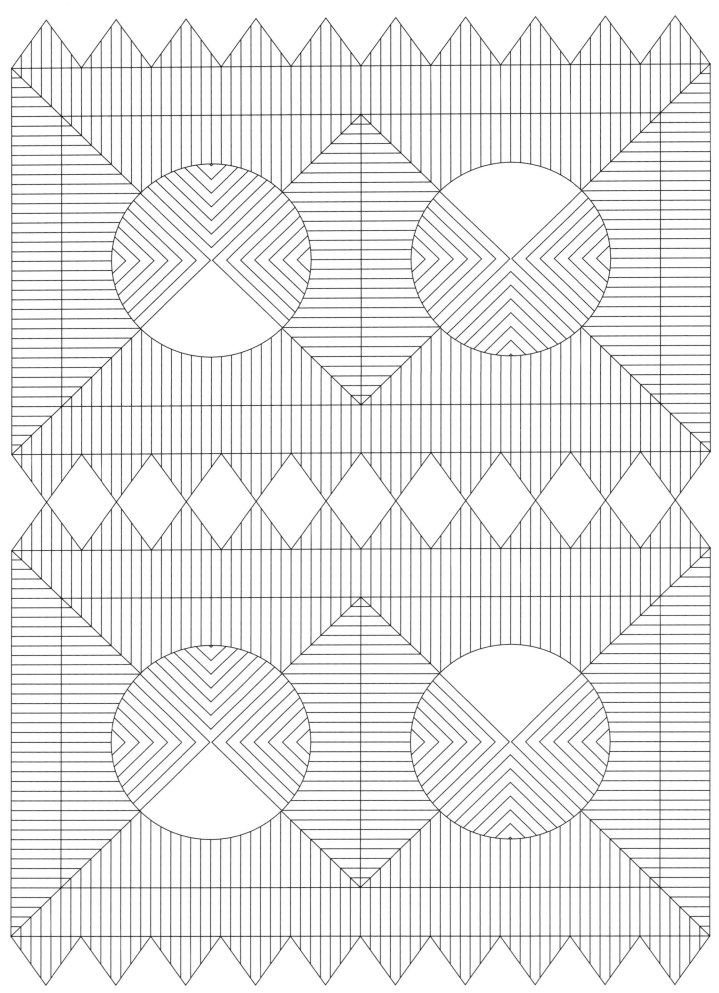

AUTOMATED

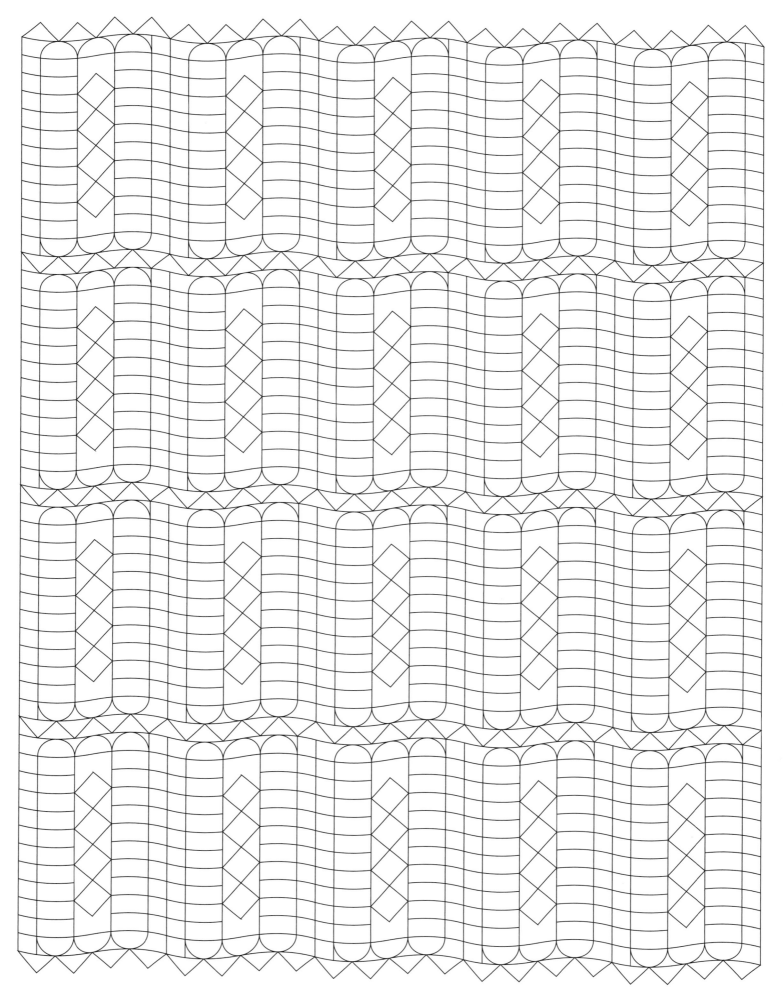

THE BIG SLIDE

PHOSPHENES

J'ADORE CONTOUR

ROBERTA'S STAR

SPIRIT

LOOPY

BEHIND EVERY GREAT STAR

AURORA

BRIGHTER PHOSPHENES

ZAPPER

PERPETUAL PETRICHOR

SONDER

FROG

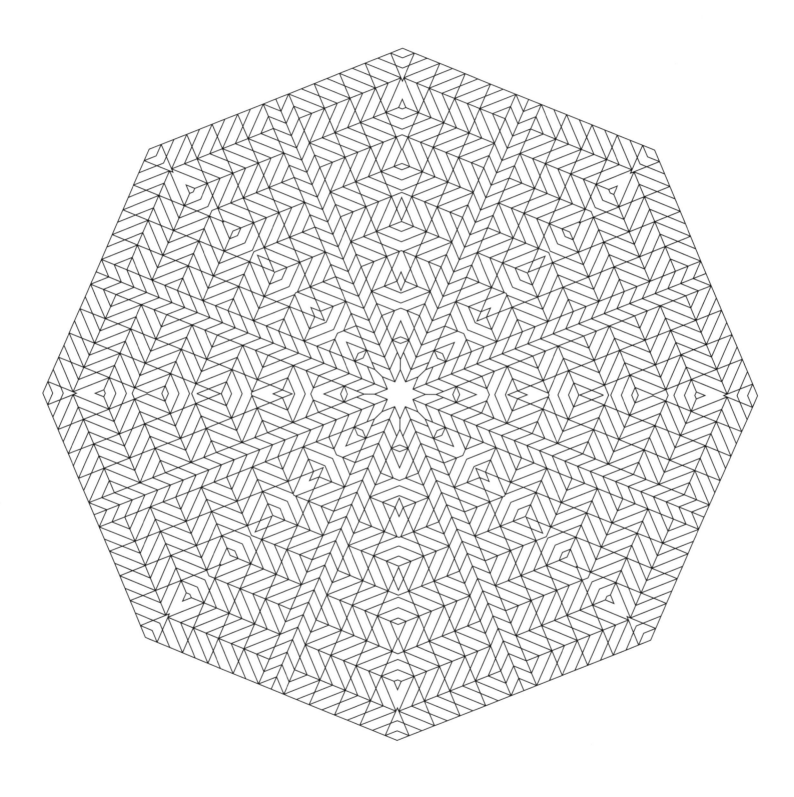

FRIEDA'S PLAY

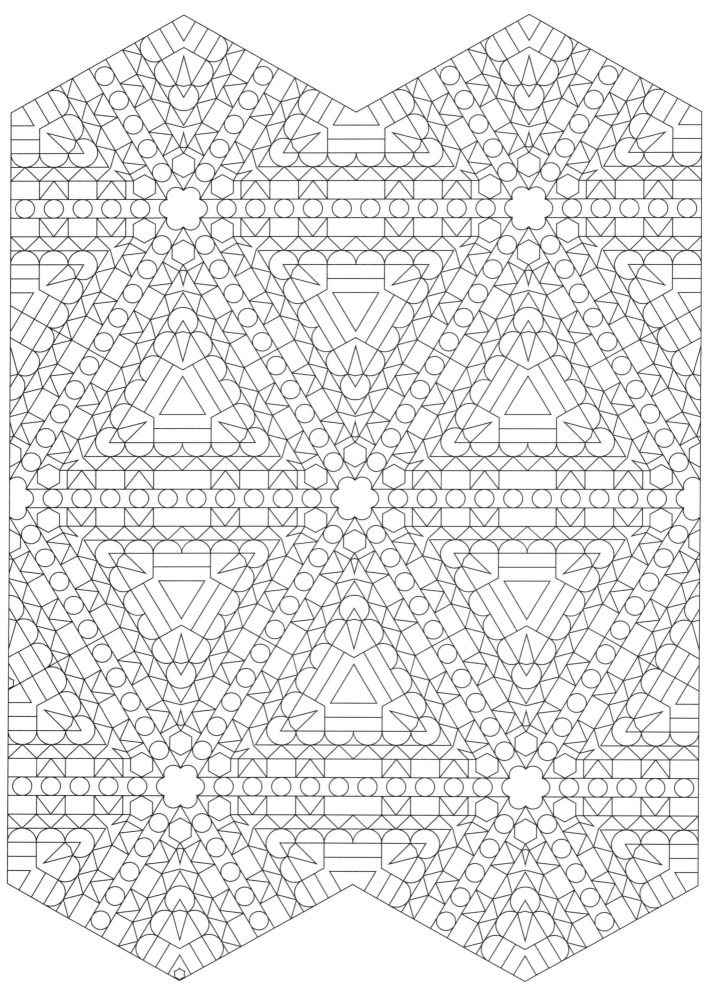

PRICKLE

JAPAN

OBI'S MAP

TODAY IS YESTERDAY

CAROUSEL

About David David

Artist and designer David Saunders graduated from Chelsea College of Art in London and assisted Tracey Emin, Mat Collishaw, and other Young British Artists before launching fashion and interiors label David David in 2007. He initially gained attention wearing his own hand-painted T-shirts to art and fashion industry parties. "I fell into fashion by accident, really," Saunders recalls. "It was just a process of who I was living with and what parties I was going to. I started making hand-painted T-shirts for myself, and people would be like, 'where did you get that from?'"

Inspired by a trip to Paris Fashion Week with friend Isabella Blow, David developed a fashion line that won him a coveted spot in London's Fashion East runway show and NewGen sponsorship from the British Fashion Council. His bold, confidently colored prints have developed over time into a distinctive, instantly recognizable style and have featured in collaborations with luxury brands including Louis Quatorze, Fred Perry, and Rimowa.

David David's 2012 collaboration with furniture designers Glass Hill appeared in the London V&A's 2012 headline exhibition "British Design from 1948–2012". The brand collaborated with Studiomama on a range of chairs nominated for the London Design Museum's Designs of the Year 2013. A 2014 commission for the London Design Festival saw David David re-tile the walls of the V&A's tunnel entrance. The current David David range includes prints, T-shirts, umbrellas, wallpaper, tableware, and scarves.

Author's acknowledgments

Thanks to Michael Sawdayee, Caitriona Row, Aoife and Frieda Sawdayee Row, Dalia Saunders, Erin and Obe Mcmillan, Menashe and Roberta Saunders, Alison Starling, Teri Olins, Toby Boundy, Maya Wild, Kathryn Ferguson, Janine Eveson, Laura Lee Pitchford, Henrietta Thompson, Jo Sherren, Gavin Foster, and Christopher Aspinall.

An Hachette UK Company | www.hachette.co.uk

First published in Great Britain in 2016 by Conran Octopus Limited,
a division of Octopus Publishing Group Limited
Carmelite House, 50 Victoria Embankment, London EC4Y 0DZ
www.octopusbooksusa.com

Distributed in the US by Hachette Book Group
1290 Avenue of the Americas
4th and 5th Floors
New York, NY 10020

Distributed in Canada by Canadian Manda Group
664 Annette St.
Toronto, Ontario, Canada M6S 2C8

ISBN 978-1-84091-738-3
Printed and bound in China
10 9 8 7 6 5 4 3 2 1

Publisher: Alison Starling
Creative Director: Jonathan Christie
Editorial Assistant: Ella Parsons
Production Controller: Sarah Kramer

Share your David David coloring at: #DAVIDDAVIDPOPCOLORING